Buyer's Price Guide

PINE FURNITURE

Compiled and Researched

by

Pamela Stewart

Edited

by

Judith and Martin Miller

Photographs

by

Peter Mould

mJm
PUBLICATIONS
Pugin's Hall
Finchden Manor
Tenterden
Kent
telephone 058 06 2234

While every care has been exercised in the compilation of this guide, neither the authors or publishers accept any liability for any financial or other loss incurred by reliance placed on the information contained.

The Publishers would like to acknowledge the great assistance given by:

Ann Lingard, Rope Walk Antiques, Rye, Sussex.
Odiham Antiques, High Street, Odiham, Hants.
Paul Fewings Ltd., 38 South Street, Titchfield, Nr. Fareham, Hants.
N. M. & T. Wilson-Chalon, Chez Chalons, 10 Church Street, Crewkerne, Somerset.
The Pine Cellars, Jewry Street, Winchester, Hants.
Mary Salter, East Street, Lewes, Sussex.
Gina Wilmshurst, Sandhill Barn Antiques, Washington, Sussex.
Jane Williams, Tenterden, Kent.
Susan March, Swigs Hole Farm, Horsmonden, Kent.
Mark Maynard, Ticehurst, Kent.
Pine Oast, Burwash, Sussex.
Jan Nelson, Pine & Design, Balcombe, East Sussex.
Pine & Country Furniture, North Street, Worthing, Sussex.
Stanley Stripped Pine, Hayne Barn, Saltwood,

Made and Printed in Great Britain by

Robert MacLehose, Scotland

CONTENTS

Introduction

Until quite recently, pine was held to be a cheap, useful timber but one which (at least as far as furniture was concerned) was quite unfit to be seen in its raw state outside servants' quarters, playrooms and the homes of the labouring classes. Certainly, it was employed in the construction of 'quality' furniture, but only in the form of a carcase which would be disguised, either by overlaying with veneers of more durable, decorative or socially acceptable timbers, or by painting and gilding in the fashion of the period.

During recent years, however, the demand for stripped pine furniture has grown enormously for a number of reasons. Reaction against the formica and chromes vogue of the late fifties caused, particularly in kitchens, a return to the country-cottagey taste which has, by degrees, been extended to influence the style of more general household decoration. Pine's warm golden colour blends with and enhances most decorative schemes and, as this was the wood used in cheap mass production at the end of the nineteenth century, it is still plentiful and easy to obtain. Stripped pine provides some eighteenth century and a great deal of nineteenth century furniture, often of excellent quality, at prices which are, by comparison with other pieces of similar age and standard, extremely attractive.

Despite the clear signs, there are many antiques dealers who deride pine furniture, and have for years dismissed its popularity as a transient fad. The facts suggest that this is not the case. For example, a solid and attractive nineteenth century chest of drawers would have retailed, in 1968, at around £12: today, the same article would cost up to £120 and is likely to continue to rise in value at the same rate as any other antique of similar age and quality.

Prices have risen dramatically, not only because of the increased demand within the United Kingdom but also as a result of the growth of the export trade. This has been felt most strongly in the South East of England, where accessability to the European buyers has resulted in increased trade with Belgium, France and Germany.

Nowadays, the increasingly widespread acceptance of pine furniture (as representing an important stage in the development of furniture in general) has led to a new awareness which, just a few short years ago, was sadly lacking. The painted pine furniture which enjoyed great popularity at the beginning of the nineteenth century is at last being spared the rigours of the stripper's tank, and the old cry of 'If it's pine, strip it' is becoming more cautiously uttered. If a piece of pine is found, painted with the pale green and rich blue backgrounds of the early nineteenth century, enriched with floral, gesso or gilt decoration, or painted and combed to simulate the colour and grain of other timbers, it is well worthwhile having it restored — provided, of course, that it is not obviously beyond redemption.

Dating pine furniture can be very hazardous. Pine was used extensively in the production of utilitarian furniture whose style was not subject to fashionable change. In consequence, a country made dresser (for example) which may have the proportions and other stylistic features of the late eighteenth century could quite easily be anything up to a hundred years younger than it at first appears. To add to the difficulty, general dating guides such as handles and feet have often been replaced; original wooden and porcelain handles, perhaps by modern brass, and bun feet with bracket feet or a brass plinth. The experienced buyer will always seek evidence, such as holes in drawer fronts and cupboard doors, that the handles have been changed, and will look carefully at the details of colour and grain in the wood of the different parts of a piece; any variation suggesting that all is not as it originally was.

The furniture shown in this book falls mainly into three categories:
1. Country pieces such as tables, chests, coffers and cupboards, which were left in their natural state and cared for by scrubbing or waxing;
2. Nineteenth and twentieth century mass-produced furniture, mainly chests of drawers, chiffoniers, sideboards, wardrobes, dressing tables, washstands, dressers and cupboards, which were gloss painted, stained or veneered;
3. Eighteenth century fitted furniture, such as barrel backed corner cupboards, architectural bookcases and shelves, and fine fire surrounds, which was custom-made and built into the large houses of the period, being painted to match the decor of the rooms of which it formed part. Due to its size and construction as part of the room, much furniture of this kind has been broken up for removal and burned during the course of conversion of the buildings with which it was associated.

Furniture from all three categories can still be bought in virtually any condition, from the roughest 'garden shed' state to the carefully stripped, restored and highly waxed pieces which deserve a pride of place in any home. As the popularity of pine has increased, a thriving industry has grown to convert the one to the other. As with any other industry, there are jealously guarded techniques developed by professionals for their own use, and there are backyard methods which any amateur can adapt to his own purposes. Satisfactory restoration always requires skill and special knowledge, but simple stripping, sanding and waxing lies well within the capabilities of anyone, though it is a messy, tiresome business, rarely undertaken more than once by any but the most enthusiastic. Although caustic soda can be used for home stripping, the material is extremely dangerous and is therefore less to be recommended than one of the proprietary brands of paint stripper.

Since the top of any piece of furniture is generally more likely to have suffered damage than its other parts, it is advisable to strip this first; unless its condition is acceptable, it is unlikely to be worthwhile continuing with the operation. Always wash down liberally with clean water after the stripping has been completed, since any residual stripper left in the wood will have a deleterious effect upon the finish. Once the piece has dried, a thorough sanding – with the grain and never across it – is necessary. The final result will always reflect the care which has been taken over the sanding, and this should always be finished with the finest grade of flour paper. Perfectionists will, having made the piece perfectly smooth, wet it to raise the grain and, after it has dried, repeat the final sanding with flour paper. There are a number of wax polishes to be had, some having a slight colour, which may enhance the richness of pine. The first coat of polish is best applied liberally with OO gauge wire wool, which will work the wax well into the grain of the wood. This will normally be followed by anything from two to six further applications of polish, depending upon the porosity of the wood.

In the past commercial pine strippers all used caustic soda in tanks large enough to entirely immerse the object being stripped. More recently, however, the chemical industry has developed a number of preparations which are enjoying widespread commercial use but are not available on the retail market. The new treatments have a number of advantages over the caustic method, not least of which is their safety to man and materials. There is still the large tank filled with tepid and steaming liquid but here the similarity ends. Now the average piece of furniture will be immersed for just one to two hours before being lifted out and cleaned with pressurised steam. This neutralises the paint softening chemicals and removes all vestiges of paint quickly and easily from tricky corners and intricate mouldings – both high-risk areas with the old, caustic method. A major benefit arising out of the relatively short immersion time is that of preserving the piece intact. No longer do mouldings fall off in the tank, and the piece that enters entire and leaves the tank as a random pile of planks should be a thing of the past.

After steam cleaning, furniture is left to dry naturally, since forced drying is certain to damage any piece to some degree, and can cause terminal cracking and warping in old, delicate or poor quality timbers. Once dry, the piece will be examined for any burn marks or other defects which require restorative work. Should this be necessary, it will be responsibly carried out and the piece once again immersed in the stripping tank. Since all chemicals used affect the colour of the wood to some degree, the second immersion has the effect of matching the colour of the repairs to that of the surrounding timber.

Anyone who has seen a piece of furniture stripped with caustic and not properly neutralised will recognise the crystalline 'bloom' which invariably grows on the surface of the timber and is a source of trouble ever afterwards. The new chemicals used cause no such problems. Once dry, furniture stripped in a modern plant can be immediately sanded and polished with complete confidence.

As to cost, it is a surprising fact that the average Do-it-yourselfer will spend more on commercial paint stripper than she would be charged by a commercial firm for the finished job. The average charge for stripping, say, a chest of drawers will be in the region of £8, while a wardrobe should cost no more than £15 to £20 to strip, depending on size. When the other factors, such as labour and mess are taken into account and added to the probable difference in standard of workmanship and its effect upon the value of the piece in question, there can be no doubt that the logical course is always to have pine stripped commercially.

In this context, it would be fair to say that, without the commercial stripping firms, the current popularity of pine furniture would never have occurred, and it is largely due to their expertise and responsible attitude that we are able to enjoy the wealth of variety of pine at the prices that we do today.

Throughout this book, the greatest possible care has been taken to ascribe realistic values to the items shown. Nevertheless, it must always be borne in mind that a book of this kind can never be more than a guide; individual dealers in different parts of the country will price their goods according to availability and demand, and such factors as quality of workmanship, state of preservation, degree of restoration, colour of wood and, not least, the age and individuality of a piece, will all materially affect its value in a rising market.

There can be no doubt that pine furniture will continue to rise in value as time passes, and already the more important pieces are beyond the pocket of many collectors. Nevertheless, there are still many items which, by comparison with other antiques, are undervalued.

These offer tremendous scope, profit potential and simple pleasure to those who enjoy seeking out treasure in auction rooms, markets and antiques shops of all kinds.

DRESSERS

In earlier days, food preparation was commonly carried out on the Dresser Board; a table set against a wall below shelves which carried stocks of necessary ingredients. By the late seventeenth century, shelves and table had been combined into a single piece of furniture — the Dresser as we know it today. This usually incorporated a Potboard or Cupboards below the table, and the narrow shelves above were used both for storage and display — though the essentially functional nature of the piece was reflected in its unornamented appearance.

Early in the eighteenth century, drawers began to be incorporated below the working surface, and the addition of a simple classical cornice anticipated the more elaborate decoration which was to follow.

By the nineteenth century, the Dresser was considered an essential household article, especially in farmhouses and cottages where it also combined the functions of China Cabinet and Sideboard. It is generally upon these later examples that we find applied mouldings and decorative turnings.

Dressers have regional characteristics
Irish Dresser: often crudely constructed, with close-boarded backs to the rack shelves, and shaped frieze to the cornice. The base with three cupboards, or two cupboards flanking a fiddle front. Solid plinth or bracket feet.

Scottish Dresser: resembles a chiffonier. No rack shelves, but a row of spice drawers at the base of a low back-board. Often having cushion moulded drawers above two or three cupboards. Solid plinth or four turned feet.

North Country and Midlands Dresser: very often without rack shelves but with spice drawers at either end of a low back-board. Larger types may have a range of drawers in the base, flanking a break-front central cupboard. Smaller types will have a range of three drawers in the base, alongside a cupboard. Side pillars of the base decorated with applied pendant split moulding.

West Country Dresser: glazed, shelved cupboards above, and drawers and cupboards below. Very decorative, with bobbin and cottonreel turned mouldings to sides, drawers and cornices.

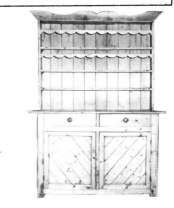

A small Irish Pine Dresser with restored cornice. 78in. high, 54in. wide. £325-350

A 19th C. pine Irish Dresser with reeded columns, two drawers and two cupboards, all in totally original condition. 96 in. high, 67 in. wide. **£250–300**

A one-piece narrow 19th C. Irish Pine Dresser with two drawers and two cupboards. 54in. wide, 78in. high. **£260-300**

An unstripped Irish 19th C. Pine Dresser base, with panelled doors and applied moulding. 66in. wide, 18in. deep. **£200-230**

A 19th C. Pine Diamond Glazed China Cabinet, with shaped shelves over four base drawers, with chamfered corners to showcase and base, 3ft 6in. wide, 6ft 4in. high. **£375-475**

A 19th C. Irish Pine Dresser with fantail carving, two drawers and two cupboards below, 5' wide, 6' high, 18" deep. **£450-470**

A Victorian Pine Glazed Cabinet, with breakfront cornice and applied pearwood pillars, the cushion moulded drawers with gothic arched door underneath to match glazed doors, 52in. wide, 76in. high. **£450-550**

A Victorian Pine Astragal-Glazed China Cabinet, with bobbin turned mouldings, panelled ends and bracket feet. 76in. high, 56in. wide. **£550-650**

A 19th C. Glazed Dresser, with one drawer and two cupboards below, 75" high, 37" wide, 17" deep. **£400-430**

A Victorian Pine Open Rack Dresser, with glazed doors in rack and base and wide dentil moulding to the base of the cornice. 5ft 6in. wide, 7ft 6in. high. **£750-850**

A 19th C. small Pine Dresser, with glazed doors to top, 78" high, 36" wide, 13" deep. **£134-145**

A 19th C. Pine Dresser with glazed doors, three drawers and two cupboards centre panel beaded in oak, 8' high, 6' wide. **£320-350**

A 19th C. Pine Cornish Glazed Dresser with split applied moulding and panelled doors and ends, 6ft 3in high, 4ft 9in wide. **£545-585**

A 19th C. Devonshire glazed Pitch Pine Dresser with quadriform moulding and fielded panelled drawers. 52in. wide, 82in. high, 19in. deep. **£595-620**

A 19th C. glazed Cornish Pine Dresser with turned side rails and four drawers with porcelain handles, 6'3" high, 4'5" wide, 19" deep. **£375-395**

A small 20th C. Dresser, Glazed Cupboard above with turned supports and cupboard below, 7'6" high, 3'6" wide. **£265-285**

An early 19th C. Irish Pine Dresser with breakfront cornice and cotton-reel moulding to sides. 6ft.3in. high, 4ft.6in. wide. **£500-550**

A 19th C. Pine West Country small cottage glazed dresser with cupboards below and applied split mouldings, 6'3" high, 4' wide, 18" deep. **£248-278**

A late Georgian Pine Concave Pot Board Dresser, with close boarded back and moulded front rack, 5ft wide, 6ft 8in. high. **£550-650**

A 19th C. West Country Pine glazed China Cabinet with arcaded panelled ends matching the doors, and applied turned and carved pillars, peg joined throughout. 5ft.4in. wide, 6ft.4in. high. **£550-650**

A small, early 19th C. Pot Board Dresser with close-boarded back and two drawers, 82 in. high, 50 in. wide, 21 in. deep. **£230—250**

15

18th Century Dresser in two pieces with three drawers and three cupboards 68 in. wide 85in. high 18in deep **£300-400**

A 19th C. Scottish Pine Dresser with applied bullseye moulding on the pediment and a bevelled mirror on the centre cupboard. 51in. wide, 20in. deep, 85in. high. **£375-395**

A 19th C. Pine Dresser base with very attractive moulding. 60in. wide, 30in. high. **£180-200**

A 19th C. English Pine Dresser, with three drawers and three cupboards, 76" wide, 84" high, 18" deep. **£190-220**

19th C. pine Dresser with four drawers above fielded panel cupboard doors. 72 in. wide, 78 in. high. 22 in. deep. **£350–400**

A pretty Victorian Dresser, with shaped sides and panelled cupboard doors, 76" high, 47" wide, 20" deep. **£350-400**

A very ornate 19th C. Pine breakfront German Dresser, 59" wide, 23" deep, 90" high. **£815-845**

A small two piece 19th C. Pine Dresser, with spice drawers and egg racks below the shelves. 43in. wide, 20in. deep, 78in. high. **£330-360**

A small narrow 20th C. Pine Dresser. 67in. high, 30in. wide, 11in. deep. **£100-130**

A small 19th C. Pine Dresser, with three long drawers with wooden turned handles, 5' high, 3' wide. **£280-300**

An early Victorian Pine North Country Breakfront Dresser Base, on six bun feet with seven drawers and a centre cupboard, 5ft wide, 36in high. **£315-365**

A small 19th C. pine Dresser with centre cupboard flanked by six drawers, standing on five turned feet. 53 in. wide, 81 in. high, 18 in. deep. **£320–350**

A 19th C. Lincolnshire sideboard with six drawers and centre cupboard. 60in. long, 54in. high. **£240-260**

A 19th C. North Country Pine Dresser, with seven drawers and a pillared door, standing on six feet. 5ft.8in. wide, 38in. high. **£325-355**

A 19th C. Pine Sideboard, with beaded and panelled doors and carved side pillars, 49" long, 38" high, 20" deep. **£230-270**

A 19th C. Pine Lancashire Chiffonier, with carved back and six spice drawers and panelled door to centre, 4ft 9in. wide, 5ft 6in. high. **£345-385**

A 19th C. Pine Lincolnshire Sideboard with four drawers and side cupboard, with added bracket feet. 46in. long, 33in. high, 19in. deep. **£170-190**

A 19th C. Pine Lincolnshire Sideboard with panelled cupboard doors, on bun feet. 48in. long, 49in. high. **£225-250**

A 19th C. pine Lincolnshire Sideboard on bun feet with concave open pot board flanked by two cupboards. 42 in. long, 42 in. high, 19 in. deep. **£275–290**

A late 19th C. Pitch Pine Lincolnshire Sideboard. 60in. long, 54in. high. **£170-190**

A Lincolnshire Pine Dresser with carved back board, 60" wide, 22" deep, 66" high. **£300-330**

A 19th C. Pine Sideboard, with seven drawers and centre cupboard and fielded panels to sides, 60" long, 53" high. **£230-270**

19

A 19th C. Pine Dresser base with three drawers. 72in. wide, 33in. high, 23in. deep. **£160-180**

CHESTS OF DRAWERS

During the sixteenth century it became the fashion on the Continent to build a drawer or two into the base of a lidded coffer. The idea quickly crossed the channel to Britain, but seems to have stagnated somewhat, for it was about a century later that further innovations were made. By the end of the seventeenth century, however, the chest of drawers had appeared in a form not materially different from that

A 19th C. Pine Chiffonier, with arched and moulded doors, 56" high, 39" wide, 17" deep. **£160-170**

produced today. There is an almost limitless number of pine chests of drawers to be found, in a variety of sizes and styles to ensure that prospective buyers are certain, with patience, to find exactly what they want.

A 19th C. pine Chest of Drawers in good condition, sides extended to form feet. 36in. wide, 29in. high, 19in. deep. **£130-150**

A Period Pine Chest of Drawers with bracket feet and thumbnail moulding on drawers. 3' wide, 40" high, 21" deep. **£170-200**

A Victorian pine Chest with a flight of eight drawers, on shaped bracket feet, 38 in. high, 33 in. wide, 15 in. deep. **£110–130**

An early 18th C. Pine Chest of Drawers, with four graduated drawers, moulded fronts and panelled sides with original rose head nails and peg joined, 32in wide, 32in high, 22in deep. **£550-650**

A small 19th C. pine Chest of Drawers with mahogany handles and gesso mouldings 36 in. wide, 30 in. high, 18 in. deep. **£90–100**

A 19th C. Pine Chest of Drawers with oak lined drawers. 40in. wide, 41in. high, 19in. deep. **£105-115**

Victorian pine Chest of five Drawers with mahogany handles, standing on high turned feet. 38 in. wide, 37 in. high, 18 in. deep. **£110-135**

19th C. pine Chest of Drawers with shaped base and mahogany handles. 36 in. wide, 29 in. high, 19 in. deep. **£95–110**

CHESTS OF DRAWERS

An early 19th C. Elm and Pine Chest of Drawers. 31in. high, 29in wide, 17in. deep. **£120-140**

A Victorian pine Chest of Drawers with new handles, 42" wide, 42" high, 21" deep. **£115-135**

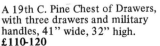

A 19th C. Pine Chest of Drawers, with three drawers and military handles, 41" wide, 32" high. **£110-120**

An attractive Victorian Pine Chest of Drawers with rounded side columns and three panelled drawers, 36" high, 42" wide. **£110-120**

A 19th C. Pine Chest of Drawers, with three drawers and mahogany handles, 30" high, 40" wide. **£90-110**

An Edwardian pine Chest of Drawers with galleried top and porcelain handles. 44 in. wide, 51 in. high, 21 in. deep. **£120–140**

A Scottish Pine Chest of Drawers with one deep top drawer made to appear as five small drawers, 3'8" wide, 3'10" high. **£180-200**

A late 19th C.   Serpentine-fronted chest of Drawers, with splashback and applied split turnings, 39" wide, 48" high. **£150-200**

A small, 19th C., pine Scandinavian Chest of Drawers, with reeded columns, panelled centre drawer and shaped plinth. 36 in. wide, 30 in. high. **£160−180**

19th C. pine Double Chest of Drawers on turned feet. 60 in. wide, 32 in. high, 21 in. deep. **£150−200**

A 19th C. Scandinavian Pine Chest of Drawers with original finger-pull holes and fluted carving on top drawer. 38in. wide, 19in. deep, 35in. high. **£135-145**

Victorian pine Chest of Drawers, recently painted with ship designs. 44 in. high, 48 in. wide. **£100-120**

A 19th C. Scandinavian Pitch Pine Chest with split turned decorations to side and original small brass handles. 3' wide, 19" deep. **£110-130**

23

A 19th C. Pine Kitchen Chest.
34in. high, 48in. wide, 18in. deep.
£100-130

An early 19th C. Pine Bow
fronted Chest of Drawers with
brass handles, 41" wide, 37" high.
£175-220

A 20th C. Pine Chest on Chest
with military handles, 18" deep,
49" wide, 37" high. **£110-120**

A 19th C. Pine Chest on Chest
with beaded drawers and swan
neck handles, 44" wide, 57" high.
£320-350

A 19th C. Pine Chest of Drawers,
with five drawers all green baize
lined each one locking, 36" high,
31" wide, 18" deep. **£110-130**

A 19th C. pine Specimen
Chest with a flight of ten
drawers with mahogany handles.
28 in. high, 12 in. deep. **£150-200**

FLIGHTS OF DRAWERS

Flights of small drawers are among the most collectable pine pieces, being both useful and (usually) attractive. Most were originally made as spice drawers for domestic use, or as storage drawers for shops and craft workshops. Where they are found still with their original paintwork — especially painted labels — they should never be stripped.

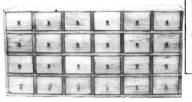

One of a pair of 19th C. Pine flights of chemist's drawers. 48in. long, 24in. high. **£190-220 pair.**

A flight of specimen drawers 48 in. wide, 8 in. deep. **£150-180**

A chemist's 19th C. Pine Flight of Drawers, with turned and dished handles. 24in. high, 26in. wide, 10in. deep. **£75-85**

A 19th C. Flight of Cobblers Drawers, with original mahogany handles, 21" high, 25" wide, 10" deep. **£90-95**

A 19th C. Flight of 8 Drawers, in Pitch Pine, with brass cup handles. 47in. high, 14in. wide, 11in. deep. **£70-75**

25

DRESSING CHESTS AND WASH STANDS

The term Dressing Chest was coined by Chippendale and redefined by Sheraton as meaning 'a small case of drawers, containing four drawers in height, the uppermost of which is divided into conveniences for dressing.'

Among the conveniences contained within the upper drawer was a hinged mirror which could be raised for use and laid flat to allow the drawer to close. Later, it became common to set a swivel mirror, perhaps above a couple of small drawers, on top of an ordinary chest of drawers.

Wash stands, too, have undergone a number of changes. Earlier examples tended to be rather elaborate contrivances, sometimes with their own water cisterns, taps and plug hole which allowed used water to drain into a bucket or bowl placed underneath for emptying at the Chambermaid's convenience. As time

passed, and running h & c found its way into the nation's master bedrooms, wash stands became simpler and plainer affairs, designed for the use of lesser members of the household.

A late 19th C. Pine Dressing Chest, with bevelled glass and porcelain handles, 42" wide, 64" high, 18" deep. **£125-135**

A 19th C. Pine Dressing Chest, with shaped base and porcelain handles, 59in. high, 33in. wide, 19in. deep. **£125-155**

A 19th C. Pitch Pine Dressing Chest, with carved mirror supports and shaped brackets below, 3' wide, 6' high. **£140-150**

A 19th C. Pine Dressing Chest with shaped back and shelf. 3' wide, 3'8" high, 20" deep. **£95-110**

A 19th C. small plain Pine Dressing Chest with mahogany handles. 3'3" wide, 4'6" high, 18" deep. **£95-120**

A pretty 19th C. Pine Dressing Table, with unusual carving to base. 35in. wide, 58in. high. **£120-140**

A 19th C. Pine Dressing Table with gesso decoration and cabriole legs. 68in. high, 48in. wide, 24in. deep. **£260-300**

An Edwardian Pine Dressing Table, with a bevelled mirror, 35in wide, 58in high. **£135-195**

A 20th C. Pine Sheraton-style Dressing Table, on castors, 3ft 6in. wide. **£185-235**

A late 19th C. Pitch Pine Dressing Table, with bevelled mirror, 56" high, 38" wide, 21" deep. **£120-130**

An early 19th C. Pine Arch-Based-Washstand, with four moulded drawers, 48in wide, 38in high. **£200-265**

A 19th C. Pine Washstand with cupboard. 30in. wide, 29in. high 16in. deep. **£65-70**

Small 19th C. pine Washstand with scalloped back and sides, turned legs and drawer to base. 24 in. wide, 34 in. high, 15 in. deep. **£35-40**

A Victorian lyre-ended Pine Washstand, with two drawers and shaped base, 38" wide, 48" high. **£110-120**

A Victorian pine Marble Topped
Washstand with two drawers,
fretwork sides and shaped centre
stretcher. 48in. wide, 38in. high.
£50-60

A Low Chunky 19th C. Pine
Washstand with one drawer.
3' wide, 30" high, 19" deep.
£60-70

A Victorian Pine Washstand with
heavily turned legs and one
drawer, 42" wide, 19" deep,
36" high. **£55-65**

A 19th C. Pine Washstand with
turned legs and shaped back
board and base. 18" deep, 3' high,
3' wide. **£55-65**

19th C. pine Washstand with high
back, two drawers, shaped frieze
and turned legs with side
stretchers. 36 in. wide, 39 in.
high, 20 in. deep. **£60-65**

A 19th C. Pitch Pine Washstand,
with shaped sides and tiled back,
with a small half moon mirror,
52" high, 43" wide, 21" deep.
£62-72

A 19th C. Pine Corner Washstand with a shaped base, 2'6" wide, 3'2" high. **£40-50**

A 19th C. Pine Corner Cupboard washstand with plug and chain. 42in. high, 27in. deep. **£90-100**

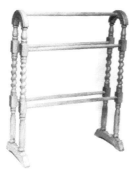

A 19th C. Hoop Towel Rail, with attractive barley twist ends. **£25-30**

A 19th C. Pine Towel Rail. **£20-25**

19th C. pine Towel Rail with double bars. **£20–25**.

18th C. pine 'winter hedge' Towel Rail. **£16–18**

WARDROBES

In mediaeval times it was the practice of noble persons to store their fine garments in the castle 'garde-robes'. This may seem unremarkable to the modern reader until it is realised that garde-robe was another name for a small indoor privy built into the castle wall and lacking the benefit of running water. The inevitable unpleasant atmosphere was the first known moth-repellent.

From such unsavoury beginnings grew the wardrobe.

Everywhere, clothes were normally stored folded in chests and linen presses and it was not until the eighteenth century that free-standing wardrobes came into popular use. Within a very short time, there were a great many styles available; from the vast, break-front, architectural types with frontages resembling Classical Temples to quite simple and attractive pieces which, in pine, fit ideally into today's taste in bedroom furniture.

A 19th C. Small Pine Wardrobe, recently painted with fairy designs. 5' high, 3' wide, 19" deep. £190-220

A large 19th C. Pitch Pine Wardrobe, inset reeded moulding to either side of door. 82in. high, 22in. deep, 49in. wide. £155-165

An early 19th C. Pine Wardrobe, with panelled doors and drawer to base, 78" high, 60" long. £400-430

19th C. satin walnut Wardrobe with narrow moulded cornice and panelled doors. 35 in. wide, 68. in. high, 16 in. deep. £100–130

31

Early 18th C. pine Joined Clothes Press, with panelled sides and 'H' hinges. 57 in. wide, 72 in. high, 20 in. deep. **£400–450**

A large 19th C. Pine Wardrobe assembled in seventeen pieces. 74in. high, 60in. wide, 25in. deep. **£390-420**

An Edwardian Pine Wardrobe with hat cupboard. 84in. high, 33in. wide. **£170-180**

A 19th C. Scandinavian seven piece Pine Wardrobe with panelled doors, with one drawer in base and standing on bun feet. 6ft.4in. high, 3ft.9in. wide, 21in. deep. **£200-250**

A 19th C. Scandinavian Pine Wardrobe with two fielded panelled doors, interior fitted with swivel pegs and a drop well in the base, 6'7" high, 3'2" wide, 17" deep. **£260-290**

A late 19th C.
pine wardrobe with
bottom drawer and
oval bevelled glass.
66in. high, 33in.
wide, 19in. deep.
130-150

A 19th C. Pine Wardrobe and
Washstand, with two drawers and
cupboard with panelled doors.
77in. high, 43in. wide, 18in.
deep. **£250-290**

An Edwardian Pitch
Pine Wardrobe, with
deep drawer to base
and porcelain
handles. 32in. wide,
78in. high. **£85-95**

BEDS

It is only since the Victorians developed the art of interior springing that beds have had, by modern standards, any real comfort. Before that time, all the attention was lavished upon the exterior structure. In deference to the universal belief that night air was filled with noxious vapours, the four-poster was developed and fitted with all-enclosing drapes for the moneyed classes — while many poorer people slept in almost coffin-shaped cupboards built into wall-recesses, with wooden doors that could be pulled shut to keep out the poisonous air and, doubtless, goblins, werewolves and other denizens of the night besides.

The beds shown here come from a later period, and as will be seen, the more interesting of these tend to be of Scandinavian origin.

A Late 18th C. Scandinavian Pine
Double Bed, with carved headboard and turned finials, 72"
wide. **£885-900**

A 19th C. pine Folding Bed with turned legs and reeded rails. 72 in. long, 24 in. wide. **£95–110**

A 20th C. Pine Bed with box sides and carved headboard. 5' 10" long, 2'6" wide. **£115-130**

A 20th C. Pine Folding Bed with reeded rails. 6'6" long, 2'6" wide **£50-70**

A Pine Victorian Bed with oak posts and legs and close boarded base, c.1850. 6'6" long, 4'6" wide. **£250-300**

A late 19th C. Cupboard Bed, probably Welsh, with new handles, open view 57" wide, 49" high, 24" deep. **£250-300**

A Swedish Pine Box Bed, with attractive finials and turned arms. c.1850-1880, 6'4" long, 3'8" high 22" deep. **£300-400**

A 20th C. Pine Swedish Bed Settle with shaped back rails, 6' long, 22" deep, 2'9" high. **£250–300**

A 19th C. pine Rocking Cradle.
£115–125

An 18th C. Pine and Oak peg joined Cradle, 39" long, 19" wide
£125-150

BOOKCASES

Although Caxton introduced the printing press to Britain before 1477, books remained rare and valuable possessions for many years, being kept locked away in libraries and, not infrequently, chained to their shelves for extra safety. It was not until the seventeenth century that books were sufficiently widely owned for furniture designers to recognise the potential market for free standing bookcases.

Originally veneered or painted to resemble mahogany or rosewood, early pine bookcases have all the style of the best furniture of their period. For modern collectors they have the added bonuses of being less expensive and more charming.

A 19th C. Pine Lancashire Bookcase on Chest, with five drawers. 76in. high, 62in. wide, 15in. deep. £450-500

An early 19th C. Irish Pine Bookcase, with two drawers above panelled doors. 102in. high. £400-450

A 19th C. small Pine glazed Bookcase with two moulded panelled doors, 6' high, 3'3" wide. 19" deep; £350-400

35

A 19th C. Pine Bookcase on Cupboard, typical marriage of two pieces of furniture. 51in. wide, 74in. high. **£185-195**

An Astragal Glazed Cornish Cabinet with two cupboards and three drawers, c.1860, 5ft. wide, 7ft. high, 18in. deep. **£500-540**

A 19th C. Pine Bookcase, with an architectural cornice and fielded panelled doors, 4ft wide, 7ft 9in. high. **£575-625**

An unusual 19th C. Pine Bureau Bookcase with gothic arched glazed doors and applied split mouldings, 84" high, 42" wide **£450-500**

A 19th C. Pine glazed Bureau Bookcase, with six interior drawers and two drawers below. 7'3" high, 3'6" wide, 19" deep. **£650-700**

A 19th C. Pitch Pine Bookcase.
58in. wide, 56in. high. £75-85

A 20th C. small Pine Bookcase
with contrasting turnings on each
set of bars, 38" high, 18" wide.
£55-75

19th C. pine Hanging Bookshelves
with shaped sides and divided
lower shelf. 26 in. wide, 39 in.
high, 8 in. deep. £45—50

18th C. pine hanging Bookshelves
with shaped sides and narrow,
reeded cornice. 35 in. wide,
31 in. high, 7 in. deep.
£70—75

An Irish Pine Dresser top,
converted to hanging
shelves, 54in. wide,
46in. high. £150-200

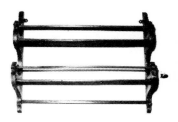

19th C. pine Hanging Shelves with
support rails and shaped sides.
26½ in. wide, 21 in. high, 6 in. deep.
£36-42

B

37

19th C. pine Hanging Shelves with shaped sides, of deep golden colour. 18 in. wide, 16 in. high, 5 in. deep. **£35-40**

A set of late 19th C. pine Wall hanging Corner Shelves with shaped sides and front. 30 in. high. **£45−60**

SHELVES AND RACKS

Small sets of hanging shelves have been in use since the sixteenth century. These were normally of very basic design, with no pretensions to elegance. During the seventeenth century, they tended to spread in width, and some attention was paid to decorative detail. It was left to Thomas Chippendale, however, to design such shelves specifically for books.

A 19th C. Pine Wall Cupboard, with two shelves, gothic arched doors and acorn moulding to cornice, 34in. high, 6in. deep. **£165-185**

A Victorian Pine Hanging Cupboard, with panelled doors and boarded sides, 6ft high, 5ft 9in. wide. **£175-250**

A 19th C. Pine Wall Cupboard, with four drawers above cupboard and applied decoration, 26" wide, 29" high, 7" deep. **£70-80**

Late 18th C. pine Hanging Wall
Cabinet with central shelf support
46 in. wide, 35 in. high, 6 in. deep
£60−70

Small, late 19th C., pine Hanging
Cupboard decorated with poker
work, having one internal, and
one external, shelf. 24 in. high,
17 in. wide.
£35−40

A small 17th C. Pine Wall Cupboard with original hinges,
23" high, 25" wide. **£110-120**

A small Edwardian pine Hanging
Cupboard with shaped back plate.
15 in. wide, 20 in. high. **£30−40**

Small, late 19th C. pine Hanging
Cupboard with new brass handle.
16 in. wide, 14 in. high.
£30−35

19th C. pine Hanging Cupboard
with galleried upper shelf and
original handle. 27 in.
wide, 19 in. high, 6 in. deep.
£35−40

CUPBOARDS

In its earliest form, the cupboard was exactly what its name suggests; a board for cups. It was usually in the form of a table or shelves which would also be used for the display of plates. Later, doors were added and, since the sixteenth century, the word cupboard has been accepted as the generic term for all items of furniture fitted with doors. Many of these, originally made for specific purposes, have retained the names which imply their old use — but few of us nowadays would reserve a bacon cupboard for the weekly pound of streaky.

A Georgian opened top Pine Corner Cupboard with fluted sides and shaped shelves. 82" high, 44" wide. **£300-320**

An 18th C. Barrel back Pine Corner Cupboard with gesso decoration to cupboard door, the dome carved out of a single piece of wood with dentil moulding to base, 84" high, 42" wide. **£900-1,200**

An 18th C. Pine Corner Cupboard with reeded columns, dentil moulding and fielded panelled doors, 84" high, 48" wide. **£750-900**

An 18th C. Barrel back Pine Corner Cupboard with reeded side columns and dome, and three shaped shelves, 42" wide, 60" high. **£650-700**

An 18th C. Pine Corner Cupboard, probably French, the grill front normally backed with material. 36in. wide, 56in. high. **£350-400**

18th C. pine Corner Cupboard with two interior shelves. 43 in. high, 33in. wide. **£150-170**

An Irish Pine glazed Georgian Corner Cupboard with two panelled cupboard doors and interior shelves. 7'4" high, 4'2" wide. **£750-800**

A 19th C. half-glazed Corner Cupboard with reeded cornice and columns, and panelled sides. 72in. high, 57in. wide. **£400-430**

A Georgian Pine Hanging Cupboard with two doors and a single hat cupboard above, 36in. wide, 56in. high. **£170-220**

An 18th C. Irish Pine Corner Cupboard with rope twist and cottonreel mouldings. Three drop drawers and shaped shelves to interior, 5' wide 7' high, 27" deep. **£700-750**

A 19th C. Pine Narrow Welsh Corner Cupboard with glazed top and cupboard below. 6'4" high, 2'6" wide. **£350-400**

A 19th C. Welsh Pine and Fruitwood glazed Corner Cupboard with two shaped shelves. 3ft.6in. wide, 6ft. high. **£300-320**

A 19th C. Pine Corner Cupboard with semi-arched moulded panelled doors. 31in. wide, 44in. high. **£200-250**

19th C. cupboard with two shelves and glazed top 45 in. wide, 56 in. high. **£110-160**

A 19th C. Pine Corner Cupboard with diagonally boarded doors and one interior shelf. 44in. wide, 31in. high. **£70-80**

A 19th C. Fruitwood Corner Cupboard, with panelled doors, 31" wide, 44" high. **£120-150**

A 19th C. Pine and Elm Corner Cupboard, with inscribed carving on each door 'God is faithful' 'Love one another', 27" high, 20" wide. **£100-140**

A 19th C. Pine Corner Cupboard, with applied moulding to door, 31" wide, 44" high. **£120-150**

A late Victorian Pine Game Cupboard, with diagonal panelled doors in the base and gauze safe doors above, 6ft 9in. high, 3ft 3in. wide. **£295-345**

A 19th C. Small Pine Hanging Corner Cupboard, 17" wide, 14" high. **£30-35**

An early 19th C. Irish Pine Food Cupboard, the drawer and re-glazed doors with wood and porcelain handles, 52in. wide, 78in. high **£385-435**

An Irish Pine Food Cupboard, with panelled doors and sides and fantail moulding to cupboard doors, c.1850, 6'6" high, 5' wide, 24" deep. **£450-500**

An Irish Pine Food Cupboard, with cats-eye moulding and arcaded and reeded interior surround, c.1840, 7' high, 5' wide, 21" deep. **£490-520**

18th Century French Pine Cupboard with original hinges and two bottom drawers 72 in. high 52 in. wide. **£500-550**

North Country Cupboard on double chest base c. 1840. 88 in. high 60 in. wide 24 in. deep. **£350-400**

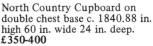

A fine 18th C. panelled pine Cupboard with four drawers in base, standing on bracket feet. 78 in. high, 60 in. wide **£400—430**

A 19th C. Pine Cupboard on Chest, with three interior shelves and four large drawers, 75" high, 22" deep, 54" wide. **£160-180**

A narrow 19th C. Welsh Kitchen cupboard with pitch pine panels on cupboard and two drawers below, with mahogany handles. 2ft.8in. wide, 7ft. 6in. high, 19in. deep. £130-160

A 19th C. Pine Linen Press, with five drawers, 77" high, 41" wide, 20" deep. £290-300

An 18th C. Welsh Pine Chippendale-style Linen Press, with blind fret top, reeded and canted corners and geometric moulded panels, the dropped well at base of cupboard with four false drawers and five drawers below, peg joined and standing on bracket feet. 6ft. high, 4ft. wide. £550-650

Plain cupboard with two shelves. 40 in. high 36 in. wide 16 in. deep. £70-80

A plain 19th C. Pine cupboard with two shelves. 40in. high, 36in. wide, 16in. deep. £70-80

An early 19th C. barred and padlocked pine Cupboard, probably used for carrying silver, with original baize lining and brass carrying handles. 28 in. wide, 18 in. high, 9 in. deep. **£45−55**

A 19th C. Pine Scandinavian cupboard with fantail moulding to cupboard doors. 4'6" high, 2'4" wide, 18" deep. **£185-210**

A small, late 19th C., pine Cupboard with one drawer and two interior shelves. 30 in. wide, 30 in. high, 18 in. deep. **£75−85**

An Edwardian Pine bedside cupboard on turned legs. 34in. high, 24in. deep, 24in. wide. **£45-55**

A narrow, late 19th. C. Pine Cupboard with panelled door. 25in. wide, 59in. high, 16in. deep. **£85-95**

A Victorian Pine Glazed Display Cabinet, with applied bobbin turnings and pierced fretted gallery, the interior lined with velvet, 3ft 9in. high, 3ft wide. **£500-550**

A small 19th C. Pine glazed Cupboard. 3' high, 2'2" wide, 9" deep **£75-85**

A 19th C. Methodist Hymn Book Pine Cupboard with brass rail around top. 45" wide, 42" high, 14" deep. **£135-145**

One of a pair of 20th C. Pine Bedside Cupboards with one drawer and cupboard below. 34" high, 24" wide, 18" deep. **£130-150 pair.**

A Small 19th C. Pine Cupboard standing on bun feet with one panelled door. 23" wide, 16" deep, 30" high. **£100-140**

An unusual Victorian Pine Cupboard, with brushing slide over fitted two door cupboard, with hinged lid-enclosed drawers. 40in. long, 32in. high, 21in. deep. **£215-245**

A 19th C. Pine Cupboard, with sliding doors and moulded panels; two shelves to interior, 59" high, 62" wide, 13" deep. **£160-170**

A Victorian Pine Cupboard, with two small panelled doors, rounded corners and black porcelain handles, 43in. wide, 30in. high. **£185-225**

SIDE TABLES

TABLES

Of all items of furniture produced throughout the centuries, few can have been made to serve such a diversity of specific purposes as the table. Size, shape, style, construction; all have been manipulated and permutated in the interests of function and fashion, from the workmanlike solidity of a thick-topped bench table to the cottagey simplicity of the pine cricket table, and from the expansive dependability of a wind-out dining table to the spinster delicacy of the spindle-legged tea tables that proliferated from the mid-eighteenth century. There are tables which inspire the writing of tender words of love and tables designed to take the sting from the loss of a fortune at cards. There are tables that stand inflexible as empires, and others that pull out, push in, swivel, tilt, rotate, fold, flap, pack up and put away as easily as politicians' promises.

A Welsh 19th C. Cricket Table in Pine and Ash. 29" diam. **£90-100**

A 19th C. Pine Tripod Tip-top Table, 18in. dia. **£145-185**

An early Victorian Pitch Pine Tilt Top Table, with block mouldings around the top, 30in. diam. **£185-235**

A Victorian Pine Cricket Table, with turned tapering legs, 18in. diam. **£95-125**

A 20th C. small occasional table with fretwork side rails and scallop edged table top. 25" high, 22" wide, 15" deep. **£30-35**

A 19th C. Fruitwood occasional table originally one of a nest of three. 16" wide, 12" deep, 27" high. **£70-90**

48

A Georgian Pine Tilt Top Tripod Table, with an ash centre column, 28in diam. **£165-215**

A small Spanish Table, with shaped side rails and one deep drawer, 24" high, 24" wide, 18" deep. **£90-120**

A Victorian Pine Tripod Table. 33in. diam. **£110-120**

A mid 19th C. Pine Console Table with heavily carved front legs and shield decoration to back, 3'9" wide, 40" high, 20" deep. **£150-175**

A 19th C. Stripped Pine Sewing Table, the exterior originally lacquered, with original lacquered fitted interior. 24in. wide, 16in. deep. **£220-250**

An Iron-stretchered 19th C. Pine Trestle Table. 54in. long, 18in. wide. **£95-115**

A 19th C. Pine Side Table, with one drawer and porcelain handles, 36" wide, 24" deep. **£45-50**

49

A large 19th C. Side Table, with three large drawers and six legs, 34" high, 91" wide, 25" deep. **£170-180**

A 19th C. Pine Bench Table, 84in. long, 23in. deep, **£120-130**

A simple, early 19th C. country made Side Table with one drawer and sturdy, tapered legs. 38 in. wide, 19 in. deep, 29 in. high. **£40–50**

Small, 19th C. pine Side Table with one drawer and turned legs. 17 in. wide 28in. long. **£32-40**

A Small Georgian Pine Side Table, on tapering legs, 23in. wide, 30in. high, 19in. deep. **£145-185**

A 19th C. Pine Side Table, with one drawer and on bobbin turned legs, 41" wide, 18" deep. **£62-72**

A small Georgian Pine Side Table, with single drawer and tapering legs, 33in. wide, 29in. high, 19in. deep. **£145-185**

A 19th C. Small Pine Side Table, with fine turned tapering legs and black porcelain handles, 35in. wide, 28in. high, 17in. deep. **£65-95**

A 19th C. Work Table with apple wood top. 78in. long, 14in. wide. **£130-160**

A 19th C. long narrow Pine Table of deep golden colour, with turned legs. 87in. long, 24in. wide, 31in. high. **£300-350**

A 19th C. Pine Table with turned rails and legs. 6' long, 2'6" wide. **£240-260**

A 19th C. Pine Irish Table with double rail, turned legs and two drawers, 5' long, 28" wide, 30" high. **£150-170**

A 19th C. Devonshire Pine Table with tapered legs and shaped top rail. 9' long, 3'3" wide, 30" high **£380-400**

19th C. pine Refectory Table with sturdy centre stretchers and supports, and shaped top rails. 60 in. long, 33 in. wide. **£130–150**

A Victorian Pine Windout Table, on large turned legs, 42" closed, 59" opened, 39" wide. **£120-140**

A small 19th C. Pine Dining Table with heavily turned legs. 5ft. long, 2ft. wide. **£85-95**

A 19th C. Pine Drop Leaf Table, with one drawer and on turned legs, 39" wide, 18" closed, 33" extended. **£60-70**

An Irish Pine Country Table, with double rail. c.1850, 4'8" long, 25" wide. **£110-150**

A large 19th C. Pine Table on castors. 42in. wide, 60in. long, 30in. high. **£145-155**

A chunky, Victorian Drop Leaf Table with one end drawer and turned legs. 30 in. wide, 17 in. closed and 34 in. extended. **£40–50**

A Welsh Pine Drop Leaf Table, with one drawer and ogee scroll each end. 30in. wide, 33in. extended. **£95-115**

A 19th C. Circular Pitch Pine Table on turned legs. 36in. diam. **£55-65**

A 19th C. Plain Pine Kitchen Table, on turned legs, 43" long, 30" wide. **£45-50**

Early 19th C. pine Kitchen Table, the two drawers with cup handles. 60 in. long, 30 in. wide. **£90-100**

A Pine Circular Dropleaf Table on slim turned legs, c.1850-1890 40" diam. **£110-170**

A 19th C. Pine Work Table, with applewood top, 78" long, 24" wide. **£130-160**

A 19th C. Pine Kitchen Table, with one gate-leg and two drawers, 42" wide, 29" high, 34" long open, 18" closed. **£75-85**

DESKS

The writing desk has its origins in the scriptoria of mediaeval monasteries. For centuries, as literacy increased, so did the variety and elegance of desks; the peak being reached during the Regency and Victorian periods. The telephone and motor car having put paid to the art of letter writing, few desks of any worth have been made since that time.

A Victorian Pine Kneehole Desk, with nine bevelled-edged drawers, 3ft 6in. wide, 19in. deep. **£345-395**

A 19th C. Pine Pedestal Desk with nine drawers, 22" deep, 46" wide. **£250-300**

54

A late 19th C. Pine Pedestal desk with nine drawers. 4' wide, 2'2" deep, 31" high. **£300-350**

A 19th C. Corn Merchants Desk in Pear Wood with six drawers and central inset cupboard. 45" wide, 21" deep, 44" high. **£295-320**

A 19th C. Pitch Pine Chart Desk 46" wide, 22" deep. **£300-350**

An Edwardian Pine Pedestal Desk; three drawers with swan neck handles and two cupboards with fielded panelled doors. 46" wide, 19" deep. **£255-275**

An early 19th C. Pine Clerks Desk with deep drop well 36" wide, 40" high, 24" deep. **£150-200**

A 19th C. Pine Estate Office Desk, with two drawers in the base, 45in high, 32in wide. **£135-185**

A 19th C. Pitch Pine Desk, with side flap and two porcelain inkwells, 36" high, 33" wide, 24" deep. **£100-110**

A 19th C. Pitch Pine Clerk's Desk. 40in. high, 21in. deep, 24in. wide. **£80-90**

An Edwardian Pine Table and flight of drawers married to make desk. 43in. wide, 21in. deep, 35in. high. **£135-145**

A late Georgian Pine Estate Desk, on tapering legs and the interior fitted with pigeon holes, 43in. high, 33in. wide. **£225-265**

A 19th C. Pine Bow-Fronted Desk, with nine drawers and gesso decoration. 53in. wide, 27in. deep. **£575-600**

A 19th C. Pine Desk, with fretwork sides, three drawers and pigeon holes, 39" wide, 21" deep. **£160-200**

A 19th C. Pine Desk Top, with fitted interior. 33in. wide, 24in. deep. **£50-55**

A Georgian Pine Escritoire, with seven interior drawers and drawer under, 33in. wide, 42in. high, 18in. deep. **£450-550**

A Victorian Pine Writing Desk, 39in wide, 39in high. **£195-235**

A 19th C. Pine Escritoire with ten interior drawers and new Chippendale-style handles and escutcheons. 56in. high, 39in. wide. **£300-350**

WHAT IS PINE?

Timber is divided, for the purpose of classification, into 'hard' and 'soft' woods. This can, in practice, be quite misleading, for it has nothing whatever to do with the consistency, strength or durability of the timber as such. Hard woods are those from (usually) broad-leaved trees; those that shed their leaves in winter. Soft woods are those which are sawn from needle-leaved, coniferous trees, of which most are loosely classified by the term pine.

A common characteristic of most pine is the striped appearance given to the wood by the annular growth rings. The dark, hard stripes indicate winter growth, while the softer, lighter parts represent summer growth. From this it follows that the hardest and most durable pine will be that which grows in the harshest conditions, with short summers to limit the growth of soft wood and long winters to increase the proportion of hard.

A 19th C. Scandinavian Pine cylinder top Bureau (awaiting handles and final polishing) with interior drawers and writing slope, 4'2" wide, 3'10" high, 23" deep, price as finished **£550-570**

COFFERS

According to the seventeenth century authority Randle Home; 'A Coffer, if it have a straight and flat cover, is called a Chest; which in all other things represents the Coffer, save the want of a circular lid or cover.' The ancient craft of Coffering having died of natural causes, no such distinction is made nowadays, and the two terms are largely interchangeable.

Basically, these are storage boxes intended for the safe-keeping of clothes and valuables and, as such, represent man's earliest endeavours in the field of furnishings and fittings. Individual needs, taste and social standing have influenced size, style, quality of manufacture and degree of decoration but the examples shown here, being of pine, are among the most utilitarian examples of their kind.

Mid 19th C. pine Mule Chest with two drawers in base and shaped plinth. 44 in. wide, 29 in. high, 20 in. deep. **£120-130**

A large 19th C. Pine Mule Chest with long drawer in base, interior fitted with candle box and two small drawers. 49in. wide, 27in. high, 25in. deep. **£135-145**

An 18th C. pine Mule Chest with two drawers in base and on bracket feet, 24 in. high, 38 in. long, 20 in. wide. **£120—140**

A 19th C. Pine Mule Chest with hinged top and two drawers beneath. 3ft. wide, 18in. deep, 2ft.2in. high. **£85-95**

Early 18th C. pine Coffer with lock missing. 47 in. wide, 26 in. high, 18 in. deep. **£130–140**

19th C. pine Coffer in exceptionally good condition, with original hinges. 38 in. wide. 19 in. deep, 19 in. high. **£50-60**

A 19th C. pitch pine panelled Coffer, the interior fitted with one deep drawer and candle box. 22 in. wide, 12 in. high, 11 in. deep. **£45–55**

A 19th C. Pitch Pine Coffer, with interior candle box, 19" high, 36" wide. **£45-50**

An 18th C. Pitch Pine Coffer, 48" wide, 25" high, 18" deep. **£120-140**

An 18th C. Pine Coffer, with sides extended to form feet. 47in. wide, 26in. high, 18in. deep. **£45-55**

19th C. pine Coffer with iron handles. 16 in. high, 37 in. wide. **£35-40**

COFFERS

An 18th C. Domed Marine Chest in pine with oak legs and original spearhead hinges. 4'6" wide, 2' deep, 34" high. **£220-240**

A 19th C. Pine Coffer with iron handles 2'6" wide, 19" deep, 18" high. **£40-50**

Early 19th C. domed Pine Coffer, with interior candle box, on bracket feet. 43 in. long, 29 in. high. **£130-150**

A 19th C. heavily moulded Pine Scandinavian Coffer, 66" wide, 20" deep. **£350-400**

An early 19th C. Coffer, with planked top and three panels. 53in. wide, 24in. deep, 29in. high. **£200-230**

An early 19th C. Pine Blanket Chest having two small drawers and candle box within. Original iron handles and strap hinges. 45in. wide, 22in. high, 21in. deep. **£80-100**

A Mid 19th C. Pine Coffer with fielded panels and flat bun feet. 54" wide, 24" deep, 27" high. **£110-120**

SETTLES

In mediaeval times, almost the only forms of seating were crude stools, benches and chests. The latter were usually placed against walls, and benches were not uncommonly fixed to the wall-panelling of lordly establishments. Once this is realised, the ancestry of the settle is immediately apparent, for it is no more than a bench or chest fitted with its own small section of wall panelling and equipped with arms. The Bacon Settle (or Bacon Cupboard) is a variation on the same theme, combining a wide, shallow cupboard with the Settle back. This was, as the name suggests, used for the storage of bacon sides and other foods.

A Somerset Settle with cupboards in the back, c.1840 5'6" wide, 5'10" high, 21" deep **£590-610**

A Small Welsh Pine Settle, with a box in the base. c.1850, 4' wide, 4' high, 20" deep. **£240-270**

An 18th C. Pine Settle with panelled back and three deep drawers in the base. 72" long 72" high. **£400-450**

A Pine peg-joined Box Settle c. 1750. 4ft. wide, 4ft. high. **£185-195**

A 19th C. Irish Pine Settle. 72in. long, 24in. deep. **£200-250**

An 18th C. Pine Settle with fielded panels. 52in. wide, 4ft. high. **£240-260**

KITCHEN CHAIRS

Designers and manufacturers of chairs have always had to face one major problem; that of combining attractive, light appearance with strength. The stresses placed upon chair backs, and upon the joinery of seat and legs (particularly by those who sit rocking on the back legs) is truly enormous. For this reason, kitchen chairs of any age should always be inspected most carefully before being bought for use. Once the back joints have come apart, they can rarely be repaired satisfactorily. Most vulnerable are those chairs whose two back uprights are jointed into the seats independently of the back legs, though the Windsor chair, with its multiplicity of upright spindles, is an example of how the load can be spread effectively for greater strength.

Kitchen Chair from Midlands. **£18** each

18th C. pine Fool's chair from Yorkshire. **£24-30**

A 19th C. Kitchen Chair with turned slats and turned and sloped side rails. **£126-130 set of six £21-26 each**

A set of four 19th C. Pine Kitchen Chairs with pierced centre splats flanked by turned splats and on turned legs. **£95-110**

A set of six 19th C. pine bar-back Kitchen Chairs. **£140–170**

A 19th C. Midlands Kitchen Chair with turned slats and scalloped back bar, **£126-130 for set of six £21-26 each**

A 19th C. Chair, with shaped back, turned legs and bobbin turned front rail. **£25-30**

A 19th C. slat back Kitchen Chair **£126-130 for set of six £21-26 each**

A late 19th C. American Pine Chair, with decorative back and turned rails. **£200-230 for set of six.**

An Irish 'fools' chair in Pine, Ash and Elm. **£50-60**

A 19th C. Plain Welsh Kitchen Chair. **£30-35**

A finely turned 19th C. Midlands Rocking Chair. **£170-200**

A 19th C. Pine Smokers Bow with turned legs and splats. **£50-60**

An Early Welsh Country Chair. **£150-170**

A 19th C. Slatback Carver. **£70-75**

A South Welsh Carver, c.1860. **£85-95**

An 18th C. Pine Welsh Lambing Chair. **£500-550**

A 19th C. Child's pine Rocking Chair with pitch pine rockers. **£55−65**

A small pine Rocking Chair with cut out heart decoration. **£55-65**

A 19th C. Child's High Chair which converts into a low rocking chair. **£75-85**

A 19th C. Pine Welsh Pig Bench, 6ft long. **£75-115**

A 19th C. Welsh Spinning Stool. 24in. high. **£25-35**

A 19th C. Pine School Ben 8' long. **£40-45**

18th C. pine joint stool with restored top. **£30-40**

An 18th C. fruitwood Milking Stool. **£40–50**

A 19th C. Pine Round Country Stool. **£15-25**

A small 19th C. elm Stool on close-turned legs. **£25–30**

An early 19th C. pitch pine Footstool. 12 in. x 6 in. **£8–10**

A 19th C. pitch pine Footstool. 12 in. wide, 6 in. deep. **£8—10**

An Early 19th C. Stool with fruitwood top and turned pitch Pine legs. 21" high. **£18-20**

Small, early 19th C., pine stool. **£10—12**

Small 19th C. stool with turned pine legs and oak top. 10 in. wide, 7 in. deep. **£8—10**

A late 19th C. Kitchen Stool in beech, with turned legs and crossed stretchers. 21 in. high. **£20—25**

A late 19th C. Beech Kitchen Stool. 21in. high. **£18-22**

67

A late 19th C. miniature Chest of Drawers, with small brass handles, 16" wide, 15" high. **£55-65**

A 19th C. Pine set of spice drawers 8" wide, 6" high. **£35-45**

A miniature Lancashire Chest of Drawers, c. 1730, with chamfered edges to drawers and brass handles, serpentine base and shaped sides, 16in. wide, 18in. high **£85-95**

A miniature Chest of Drawers, made up from old pine. 22 in. high, 24 in. long. **£70–80**

An 18th C. miniature Pine Cupboard with a fielded panel door. 16" wide, 17½" high, 10" deep. **£85-95**

A small 19th C. Pitch Pine Specimen cabinet with iron carrying handle. 11in. high, 14in. wide. **£55-65**

A set of 19th C. Pine Spice
Drawers. 7in. wide, 6 in. high, 4in.
deep. £30–40

A late 19th C. miniature Corner
Cupboard, with one interior
shelf and black porcelain handle,
18" high, 12" deep, 18" wide.
£35-40

A 19th C. Pine set of spice drawers
10" high, 6" wide. £35-40

A small 20th C. amateur made
pine cabinet, 18" high, 10" wide.
£16-20

An unusual oval fronted Pine and
Fruitwood Salt Box. £25-35

19th C. pine Wall Hanging Salt
Box with hinged lid and shaped
back plate. £18–25

A Victorian wall hanging Candle-
box with match drawer above.
£15–20 MS

A plain 19th C. Pitch Pine Candle Box. £6-8

A 19th C. wallhanging pine Candle-box with pierced trefoil decoration £10–12

A 19th C. Pitch Pine Nail Box, 14" long, 8" wide. £8-10

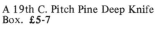

A 19th C. Pine Strong Box, with six interior compartments. £25-30

A 19th C. Pitch Pine Deep Knife Box. £5-7

A small early 19th C. domed pine box with iron handles and clasp. 20 in. long, 12 in. deep, 10 in. high. £35–45

A 19th C. Pine Tool Box, the interior fitted with trays, 19" high, 31" wide, 15" deep. £80-90

A 19th C. pine Writing Slope with hinged lid. Interior not fitted. 19 in. wide, 15 in. deep. **£25–30**

An early 18th C. Deed Box, (date on exterior added later, three earlier dates inside), original iron handles and spearhead hinges, with pegged sides to lid. **£85-95**

19th C., dovetailed pine Ammunition Box. 31 in. wide, 12 in. deep. **£20–30**

A 20th C. Pine Shoe Box, 31" high, 16" deep, 20" wide. **£45-55**

An 18th C. stripped Oak Bible Box with fine carving. The base is a 19th C. addition. 27" wide, 23" high. **£130-140**

An Edwardian Pine Coal Box, with iron carrying handle and brass side handles, 17in. wide, 18in. high. **£85-125**

MIRRORS

The first silvered-glass mirrors made in Britain superceded their polished metal forebears in 1615. By today's standards, these were of extremely poor quality.

The Victorians, on the other hand, produced mirrors which were generally of extremely high quality — many of which, bought today, are still unblemished and less costly than their modern counterparts.

Early Victorian small travelling folding mirror. £12-15

A Victorian Pine Dressing Table Mirror with carved mirror supports and carved feet. 19in. wide, 24in. high. £55-65

A small 19th C. Pine Dressing Mirror with drawer. 15in. wide, 19in. high, 8in. deep. £55-65

A Victorian Pine Dressing Mirror, with oval box in base. 15in. wide, 19in. high. £40-50

Small dressing mirror with drawer, 15 in. wide, 19 in. high, 8 in. deep. £52-60

72

A 19th C. Overmantel Mirror, with gesso decoration, 50" wide, 36" high. **£75-85**

A 19th C. Pine Overmantel Mirror. 36in. high, 33in. wide. **£50-55**

A 19th C. Pine Overmantel Mirror, with scratch carving. 34in. high, 48in. wide. **£40-45**

A Pine Carved Overmantel, with mirror in central arch and double, turned support pillars, c.1888 5' high, 4'4" 12" deep. **£245-280**

A William IV Pine Rope Twist and Carved Acanthus Mirror, 29in. high, 23in. wide. **£125-165**

A 19th C. Pine Overmantel Mirror, 42" wide. **£55-65**

MIRRORS

A 19th C pine framed mirror
30in x 30in. **£60-65**

An 18th C. English Floral
Carved Pine Frame, 44in. x 51in.
£1,000-1,500

A small oval 19th C. Pine Mirror.
£65-85

A Victorian Carved Pine Rococo
Mirror, 56in. high, 26in. wide.
£185-225

A 19th C. Wall
Mirror, with
bevelled glass and
gesso decoration on
pine surround, 32in.
wide, 45in. high.
£75-80

GUIDE TO BUYING

The process of dipping pine in a caustic solution often loosens joints
Check:
Chairs: Arms, legs and splats
Tables: Legs
Pine is a very soft wood therefore the feet of a chest of drawers, wardrobe or dressers are seldom original this sometimes applies to cornices
Check:
The colour of the addition matches the original piece
The workmanship is good and the joints not just nailed or glued together

Bureaus are often made up from old chest of drawers. The price of a made up piece should be considerably lower than an original
Check: the bureau lid and the desk interior, the wood will feel and look different and the interior will be too pristine

Chest of Drawers
Check: Drawers run smoothly
Drawer back stops are in place (it is extremely annoying when drawers disappear to the back of the chest leaving a gap in the front)
Handles (seldom original) are of good quality

One of the joys of collecting the things of the past is that of owning objects which, perhaps because the world has moved on so far and so fast, are now completely removed from the needs of everyday life. Odd fragments of carving, implements for winding wool, office and shop furniture; such items are invariably decorative and a source of pleasure for no other reason than that they invite comment and spark the imagination to flights of fancy. Many of these things can have no further practical use. Many will have been so unimportant and taken for granted that they will have not been catalogued nor written about. Yet they are still with us and, as long as collectors continue to pursue their interests, will remain so.

A 19th C. Scandinavian coopered barrel. 10in. high. **£36-38**

A 19th C. pine Harvest Barrel with iron carrying handle. 10 in. high. **£35—45**

Late 19th C. solid pine Till Box **£5—7**

An early 19th C. Abacus with pine surround and coloured wooden beads. **£10—12**

A 19th C. Pine Picture Frame, 30" wide, 30" high. **£60-65**

A 19th C. Pine Bidet, with Wedgwood bowl. 27in. long, 20in. wide. **£35-40**

A late 19th C. Pine Pulpit, 6ft. wide, 3ft. 6in. high. **£250-280**

A Victorian Pine Fire Surround with heavy turned and moulded side supports, 6' wide, 4'2" high. **£100-120**

A Fine George III Stripped Pine Chimney-Piece with later eared top, 88½ in., 225 cm. wide, 62 in., 158 cm. high. **£1,000-1,200**

19th C. pitch pine Commode with diagonal-planked front panel. **£40–45 (plants extra!)**

Pine Edwardian folding Steps, 28 in. high. **£30–40**

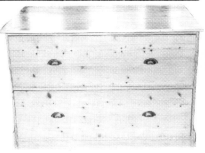

A 19th C. Pine Shop Counter, with two deep drawers. 36in. high, 32in. wide, 54in. long. **£120-140**

A Pair of 18th C. Italian Pine Candlesticks, 18" high. **£120-130 pair.**

Late 19th C. pine set of Pigeon Holes, used as display unit. 51 in. wide, 25 in. high, 12½ in. deep. **£100−125**

A 19th C. Carved Torchere, in pine and lime wood, 5ft high. **£750-850**

A late Georgian Pine Commode, with dummy drawers and bull's-eye moulding on the lid, 26in wide. **£95-135**

An early 19th C. pine Spit Rack, unpolished. 54 in. high, 60 in. wide. **£250−300**

Late 19th C. pine Shop Counter
with inset panel front. 60 in long,
32 in. high. **£70–80**

A 19th C. Wooden Winder,
(possibly used for fishing lines),
37in. high, 22in. wide. **£45-55**

An 18th C. Spanish Bowl, 18"
long, 12" wide. **£60-70**

A Wooden Winder (use unknown)
any ideas? 13" long. **£19-23**

A Threefold 19th C. Pitch Pine
Screen, with three small opening
panels. 6ft. high, 5ft. long fully
opened. **£450-500**

A 19th C. Wooden Wheelbarrow,
with a solid wooden wheel.
£100-125

A 19th C. wooden doll's sink with scrubbing brushes. Sink 9½in. long, brushes 3¼in. long. **£15-17**

A pair of early 19th C. Spanish softwood Panelled Doors with two opening inner sections. 69in high, 45in. wide. **£200-250**

19th C Pine Inkwell
£5-8

A pair of Italian stripped pine Wall Brackets **£150—200**

A Welsh Elm Nut Holder 18" long. **£10-15**

A late 18th C. carved Angel's Head, probably originally part of a pine frieze. 12 in. wide. **£150—160**

A small, late 18th C. carving of two Cherubim, probably from an Italian Frieze. 6 in. wide. **£30—50**

Three 19th C. Pine Ducks on Wheels, mother duck 7in. long, baby ducks 4in. long. **£25-35**

A 19th C. adjustable Pine Tilt-top Reading Tray Table. 33in. wide. **£145-185**

DAIRY

Old dairy items are becoming increasingly popular with collectors and, as such, have probably not yet found their true 'value-level' in the scheme of things. Many of them are both interesting and decorative — and some are still useful!

A 19th C. Oak and Pine iron bound Cheese Mould, 17" diam **£15-20**

A 19th C. Oak and Pine iron bound Cheese Mould, 17" diam. **£15-20**

A 19th C. Danish Cheese Mould made in removable sections to release cheese. 13" long. **£25-30**

A 17th C. Finnish Butter Box, with wooden nails, the seams joined with woven bark, 6" long, **£45-55**

80

An 18th C. Sycamore Dairy Bowl hand turned on pole lathe. 12in. diam. **£40-45**

A good mid-19th C. Scandinavian painted pine butter tub and cover, named and dated 1849. **£180-200**

Late 17th/Early 18th C Welsh Cream Bowl in sycamore, 19" diam. **£70-100**

A collection of 19th C. wooden Butter Stamps on white porcelain butter dish. **£30–40**

An 18th C. machine turned Butter Bowl. 6in. diam. **£30-35**

A 19th C. Wooden Butter Dish, with a Glass Liner. **£6-8**

A 19th C. Butter dish inscribed 'Manners Mayketh Man'. **£7-10**

81

A 19th C. Cornish Butter Dish, stamp and Knife. **£35-45**

A 19th C. Wooden Butter Stamp, with impressed carving, **£20-25**

A Zinc-lined Pine Refrigerator, c.1870, made by Belmont, box for ice at top, 38" high, 18" wide. **£85-95**

A 19th C. Wooden Potato Masher. **£15-20**

A 19th C. Cream Whisk. **£3-6**

A Curd Cutting Knife, with Pine Handle, c.1850. **£18-20**

A 19th C. Pine Curd Strainer. **£12-14**

A butter stamp with rose mark, 1½" diam. **£15-17**

A Chunky 19th C. Pine Dairy
Table, with new handles. 30in.
high, 22in. wide, 15in. deep.
£50-55

A 19th C. Butter Churn on stand,
end over end, made by Lister &
Co., Darsley, Yorks, 12 gallon
capacity, 4' high. **£80-90**

A 19th C pine Butter Churn, with
Butter Pats. **£25—30**

A late 19th C. Earthenware Butter
Cooler with glass liner. **£3-5**

A late 19th C. earthenware Milk
Cover. **£3-5**

A wooden butter wheel, 7" long.
£15-17

BAKERY

Although the home baking of bread has enjoyed a recent vogue, it is unlikely that many households will be producing enough to warrant the use of the dough bins and proving cupboards which have survived from Victorian days.

These are now considered to be decorators' items; the dough bins used to good effect as indoor plant troughs, and the proving cupboards as sturdy storage places.

Such crudely constructed items as these are not to everyone's taste but, owing to their relative scarcity (when compared with the abundance of more formal furniture) they do now, and will continue to, command very respectable prices on the open market.

A 19th C Pine Bread Proving Cupboard on original castors 41" wide, 48" high. **£120-140**

A 19th C. Pine Bread Proving Cupboard with double door 54" high, 43" wide. **£150-160**

A 19th C. Pine Baker's Bin with opening front. 60in. long. **£250-270**

A late 18th C. Elm Dough Bin. 60in. long, 30in. deep. **£235-265**

A 19th C. Pine Grain Scoop. **£10-12**

A 19th C. Dough Bin with cover. 65in. long, 31in. deep. **£45-55**

A 19th C Bread Board with ears of wheat carving. **£7-10**

An Edwardian pitch pine Flour Bin on bun feet. **£45–55**

A 19th C. Wheatsheaf Design Bread board and knife. **£20-25**

A Victorian pine Corn Measure 12 in. high. **£45–50**

A Victorian enamel Bread Bin. **£6-8**

Victorian pine Flour Bin with lid and wooden hoop handle. **£25–30**

A 19th C. Scandinavian Bread Slicer made of wood and iron. 11in. long, 7in. wide. **£18-22**

KITCHEN

For a number of years there has been a growing interest in the kitchen utensils of the past. Decorative, sturdy and in many cases more practical in use than their modern counterparts, such items are certain to retain their popularity. This is an area of collecting where specialisation will pay dividends.

18th C Brass flour sifter. **£60-65**

An 18th C. Welsh spoon rack. 27in. wide, 31in. high. **£130-140**

A 19th C. Pine Spice Rack, 30in. high, 24in. wide. **£185-235**

A 19th C. Irish Pine Mug Rack, 36" wide, 37" high. **£90-100**

An 18th C. Pine Spice Rack, 39" high. **£110-130**

Late 19th C. pine Meat Safe. Close wire mesh panels in sides and doors and one internal shelf. 35 in. high, 37 in. wide, 25 in. deep.
£45-50

Late 19th C. pine Meat Safe with close wire mesh panels in sides and and single door. One internal shelf. 22 in. wide, 16 in. high, 16 in. deep.
£28-35

A Shelley swan mould in white china, 8" long. **£20-23**

A 19th C. Flight of Pine Spice Drawers, 27" high, 18" wide, 18" deep. **£90-95**

A 19th C Earthenware Jelly Mould with lion shaped base. **£12-14**

Three 19th C. miniature Copper Jelly Moulds, 2in. high. **£10-12** each

87

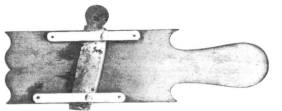

A 19th C. Cucumber Slice. £25-30

A 19th C. pine wall hanging Kitchen Plate Rack. £5−8

A 19th C. Pine Plate Rack, with shaped sides. £40-45

A 19th C chopper. £6-8

A 19th C. Pine Plate Rack, 2'6" high. £34-40

A 19th C. Pine Hanging plate rack. 22in. high, 14in. wide. £19-25

A 19th C. Pine Plate Rack. 22in.
high. £35-40

A 19th C. Pine Plate Rack.
£20-25

A Victorian sardine tin opener,
5" long. £8-10

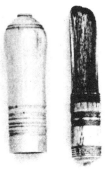

18th C bone cheese scoop. £20-
30

A 19th C. Iron Lemon Squeezer.
£16-18

A 19th C. wood and china Lemon
Squeezer. £17-19

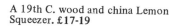

A 19th C Tin Strainer, 4" diam
£3-5

19th C wood pastry marker.
£4-8

An Early 19th C. Wooden Ladle
£30-35

A Besway knife cleaner, 19th C,
9½" high. £15-17

Iron Goffering Iron, 7" high. £15-18

An Early 19th C. Smoothing
Iron. £33-36

Adjustable Scales. £13-15

A Brown and Polson Blanc-mange
bowl. £15-17

An Iron Knife Cleaner, 15 in. high, c. 1850. **£32-40**

A glazed basket weave Game Dish, 8½" long. **£75-85**

A Selection of 19th C. Corkscrews. **£17-24**

A Bone and iron corkscrew. **£25-28**

(l) A Brass Barrel Corkscrew with ivory handle and coat-of-arms, c1840. **£95-105**

(r) A Brass Barrel Corkscrew with ivory side-lever and original ebony handle, c1840. **£110-120**

A Corkscrew. **£4-6**

An Iron Corkscrew. £9-10

A set of 1920 Storage Jars with wooden lids. £5-7 each

A Victorian MacFarlane and Lang Biscuit tin. £4-6

A Victorian Pine Four-Tiered Buffet, with two drawers, 48in. wide, 57in. high. £215-245

A Tea Tin with Chinese design. £2-4

A 19th C Mouse trap, 4½" long. £4-5

19th C. pine Vegetable Rack with four compartments of varying depths. Sturdy construction. 36 in. high, 15 in. wide. £35–40

Early blue and white china Egg Stand. **£15-17**

A C.C. Clark and Co. of Wolverhampton cast iron Coffee Grinder. **£40-45**

An Iron bound wooden tig, 19th C. **£30-35**

A set of small Victorian wooden measures, ½pt., 1pt., 1 quart. **£25-30**

A Wooden Meat Dish with gravy channel. **£15-17**

A 19th C. bucket-shaped pine Ice Cream Maker, iron bound with carrying handle. **£40—50**

Adam Style; influenced by the classical revival initiated by the architect Robert Adam (1728–1792)

Applewood; English fruitwood, of a reddish brown colour.

Applied Mouldings; carved, shaped edges to panels, cabinets and chests for decorative effect.

Apron; shaped piece below a chair's seat rail, or base rail between the legs of a cabinet, usually treated ornamentally.

Architrave; the moulded frame surrounding a door-way.

Aumbry or Ambry; one of the first types of cupboards with doors, sometimes recessed in wall.

Bas – Relief; carved in low relief on gesso or wood.

Bead or Beading; small, half-round moulding, also called Astragal.

Boss; carved ornament that covers intersection of the ribs in a roof.

Breakfront or Broken Front; centre section projecting beyond the sides, very common in bookcases of the 18th and 19th centuries.

Burr; a growth on the trunk of a tree, which gives exquisitely marked wood for decorative purposes.

Chamfer; surface of a bevelled angle.

Cock Beading; small bead moulding applied to drawer fronts, popular through Georgian period well into 19th Century.

Cornice; the projecting moulded upper member, frequently of a bookcase or cabinet.

Cricket Table; a small three legged table normally quite plain.

Deal; a general term for the wood of coniferous trees.

Dough Bin, Bread Trough, Kneading Trough; in common use from mediaeval times to the 19th Century. It was a trough of table height standing on 4 splayed legs. It had compartments for dry flour and dough and when covered could be used as a table.

Dowel; a peg for locking a joint together.

Fielded Panel; panel with the central area raised above the frame, surrounded by bevelled or chamfered edges.

Gesso; a composition of plaster used as a medium for carved decoration.

'In the white'; furniture in its raw unpolished state.

Kas; term used for a large upright cupboard (term of Dutch origin).

Linenfold Panelling; a stylized representation of linen in folds invented in the 15th Century.

Ogee or Ogive; moulding with a double curve, convex below, concave above.

Patina; the surface colour and finish of wood caused by generations of polish and age and use. N.B. but can be simulated.

Pitch Pine; a pine from North America, with a distinctive yellow colour.

Satin Walnut; a soft yellow wood used for mediochre Victorian furniture, also known as American Red Gum.

Scroll Moulding; moulding resembling a scroll of paper, most prevalent in the Gothic revival furniture of the 19th Century.

Smoker's Bow; really a simple version of the low-backed Windsor chair which became very popular in the 19th Century.

Smoker's Chair; an upright armchair with an automatic drawer below the seat which contained a metal spittoon.

Splat; the central upright part of a chair-back.

Trellis-Work; a form of lattice work.

Veneer; basically a thin second skin of walnut, rosewood or mahogany applied normally by glue to an inferior wooden carcase.

Victorian Period;
1837 – 60 Early Victorian
1860 – 80 Mid- Victorian
1880 – 1901 Late Victorian

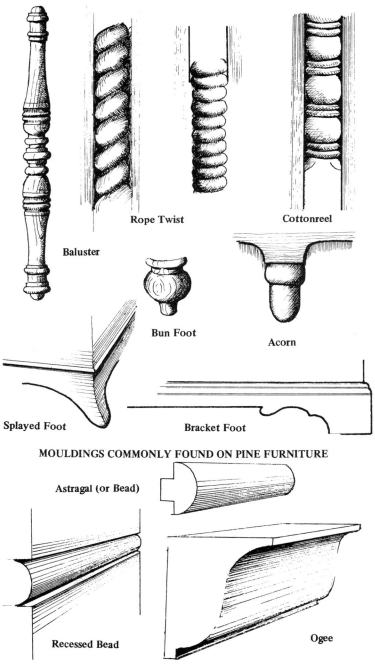

SOME SPLIT TURNINGS APPLIED TO PINE FURNITURE

Rope Twist

Cottonreel

Baluster

Bun Foot

Acorn

Splayed Foot

Bracket Foot

MOULDINGS COMMONLY FOUND ON PINE FURNITURE

Astragal (or Bead)

Recessed Bead

Ogee

LONDON

Pine Prestige
Grays Mews, 1-7 Davies Mews C31/32
Princedale Antiques
70 Princedale Rd., Holland Park,
London W.11.
Hallidays Carved Pine Mantelpieces
Ltd., 28 Beauchamp Place,
London S.W.3.
Isabelle Collins
154 Wandsworth Bridge Road,
London S.W.6.
Richard Morris Antiques
136-142 Wandsworth Bridge Road,
London S.W.6.
Old Pine
545-571 Kings Road, S.W.6.
The Pine Warehouse
162 Wandsworth Bridge Road,
London S.W.6.
Pine & Design Gallery
28 Shelton St., Covent Garden W.C.2.
Scallywag
Wren Rd., Camberwell Green, S.E.5.
Silver Sixpence
14 Catford Hill, S.E.6.
Peckham Pine Antiques
80 Peckham Rye, S.E.15.
John Creed Antiques Ltd.
3-5A Camden Passage, N.1.
The Pine Shop
12B Camden Passage, Charlton Place,
Islington N.1.
Country Pine Ltd.,
13 Chalk Farm Rd., N.W.1.
Westward County Antiques
65 Chalk Farm Rd., N.W.1.
Woodworks
Camden Lock, Commercial Place,
N.W.1.
Savile Pine
560 Kings Road, S.W.6.
Sophisto-Cat
190-192 Wandsworth Bridge Road,
S.W.6.
Southbank Pine
258 Battersea Pk. Rd., S.W.11.
Gothic Country Antiques
70 Station Rd., Barnes, S.W.13.
Joy MacDonald
50A Station Rd., Barnes S.W.13.
Remember When
7 Rocks Lane, Barnes, S.W.13.
Terrace Antiques
3A The Terrace, Barnes, S.W.13.
Buttons Antiques
1597 London Rd., Norbury and
457/459 Streatham High St., S.W.16.

GREATER LONDON

J. M. Sellars Antiques (Pine),
28 St. James Rd., Croydon.
Van Broek Services
75 Station Rd., Hampton, Middlesex.

AVON

G. Leonard
Stand 60-63 Great Western Antique
Centre, Bartlett St., Bath.
Quest Antiques and Pine
27 Walcot St., Bath.
Riberac Period & Reproduction
Pine, Beech Rd., Box Hill, Bath.
Widcombe Antiques and Pine,
9 Claverton Buildings,
Widcombe, Bath.
Third Eye
4 Upper Maudlin St., Bristol.

BEDFORDSHIRE

Yesterday's Pine
13 Dunstable St., Ampthill.
Bell Antiques
15 Wing Rd., Linslade,
Nr. Leighton Buzzard.

BERKSHIRE

The Craftsman
16, Bridge St., Hungerford.
Ann Bye Antiques
88 London St., Pangbourne.
Woodbine Cottage Antiques
Bath Rd., Woolhampton, Nr. Reading.

BUCKINGHAMSHIRE

Liz Quilter
38 High St., Amersham.
Virginia House Antiques
High St., Nr. Newport Pagnell,
Sherington.

CAMBRIDGESHIRE

Longstanton Antiques & Pine
92 High St., Longstanton.
Pidley Pine Antiques Ltd.
The Cottage, Warboys Rd., Pidley.
Trislillian Antiques
51 High St., Stretchworth,
Nr. Newmarket.

CHESHIRE

Royles
2 Shaw Rd., Stockport.
Shirley Eaton Antiques
15 London Rd., Cheshire.
Richmond Galleries
1st Floor, Watergate Buildings,
New Crane St., Cheshire.
Antiques and Old Pine,
339 Oxford Rd., Macclesfield.

Peter A. Curbishley
30 Pillory St., Nantwich.
In-Tique
8 Welsh Row, Nantwich.

CORNWALL
Amamus Ltd.,
Country Antiques
Fore St., Grampound, Nr. Truro.
Old Palace Antiques
Quay St., Lostwithiel.
All Things Bright and Beautiful
Old Sunday School,
Cape Cornwall St., St. Just.

CUMBRIA
Antiques
101, Main St., Sedbergh.

DERBYSHIRE
Pottery & Pine
Station Rd.,
Spinnerbottom, Birch Vale.
Antique & Old Pine
Lidgate Farm House, Eccles Rd.,
Chapel-en-le-Frith.
Old Pine Barn
Rowan Farm, Highgate Rd., Hayfield.
Old Pine Antiques
1 Macclesfield Rd., Whaley Bridge.

DEVONSHIRE
Portobello Corner
3 Cross St., Barnstaple.
Fine Pine Antiques
Woodlands Rd., Harbertonford.
Skeaping Gallery
4 Kilworthy Hill, Tavistock.
Richard Bowyer Antiques
8-10 Barrington St., Tiverton.
Fine Pine Antiques
High St., Totnes.
Country Cottage Furniture
Yealmbury Hill, Yealmton,
Nr. Plymouth.

DORSET
Paul Bordessa
847 Christchurch Rd., Boscombe,
Bournemouth.
Old Forge Antiques
Station Rd., Stalbridge,
Nr. Sturminster Newton.

ESSEX
Trevor Jones Antiques
18a Rayne Rd., & Unit 6,
Springwood Drive, Braintree.
Bits & Pieces
Church Hill,
Finchingfield, Nr. Braintree.
Andrew Tate
Great Wincey Farm, Finchingfield.
The Stores
Great Waltham, Nr. Chelmsford.
Newport Antiques
High St., Newport, Nr. Saffron Walden.

Neals Antiques
470-470a Southchurch St.,
Southend-on-Sea.
Pearces Pieces
High St., Thorpe-le-Soken.
Fox & Pheasant Antique Pine
Colchester Rd.,
White Colne, Nr. Colchester.

GLOUCESTERSHIRE
Bed of Roses
12 Prestbury Rd., Cheltenham.
John Townsend
2 Oxford Cottages,
Ullenwood, Nr. Cheltenham.

HAMPSHIRE
Althea Wilson
12 East St., Alresford.
Just the Thing
High St., Hartley Wintney.
David Clark
The Plestor, Selbourne, Nr. Alton.
Paul Fewings Ltd.
38 South St., Titchfield, Nr. Fareham.
The Pine Cellars
Jewry St., Winchester.
Odiham Antiques
45 Odiham High St., Odiham.
The Pine Shop
High St., Odiham.

HEREFORD & WORCESTER
Paul Davies Antiques
32 Load St., Bewdley.
Gay Walker
Birley Court, Birley.
Smiths Antiques
Aubrey St., Hereford.
G. Hill & Partners
The Red House, Kingsland.
The Old Swan Antiques Shop
44 The Homend, Ledbury.
La Barre Ltd.
Lion Yard, Broad St., Leominster.
Michael Stewart Antiques
Lion Yard, 15 Broad St., Leominster.

HERTFORDSHIRE
Parade House Antiques
72 High St., Ashwell.
Langley Antiques
15-17 High St., Kings Langley.
Flowerdale Antiques
23 High St., Markgate, Nr. St. Albans.

HUMBERSIDE NORTH
Paul Wilson Old & Antique Pine
70 Anlaby Rd., Hull.

KENT
The Village Gallery
High St., Brasted.
P. Miles, The Pine Shop
Hawkinge, Nr. Folkstone.
Ash House
18 Hereson Rd., Ramsgate.

Sevenoaks Furniture Gallery
140 High St., Sevenoaks.
Stanley Stripped Pine
Hayne Barn, Saltwood, Nr. Hythe.
Susan March
Swigshole Farm, Horsmonden, Kent.

LANCASHIRE
Martin Bond Antiques
129 St. Leonardgate, Lancaster.
Pot of Gold Antiques
1 Peel Brow, Ramsbottom.
Seek & Find Antiques
Old School Showrooms,
Old Barton Rd., Urmston.
L.G. Gough
550 Bolton Rd., Aspull, Wigan.

MERSEYSIDE
Turn of the Century
20 Lark Lane, Liverpool.

NORFOLK
The Maltings
Millgate, Aylsham.
Maltings Antiques
53 The Street,
Old Costessey, Nr. Norwich.
Priory Antiques
Litcham, Nr. Kings Lynn.
Pam Salmon & Peter Wells
9 Burnt St., Wells-next-the-Sea.

NORTHAMPTONSHIRE
Bits & Pieces
3a Church St., Finedan.
Bits & Pieces
34 High St., Higham Ferrars.
Richard Kimbell Antiques
17-19 St. Georges St., Northampton.
Thirty-Eight Antiques
62 High St., Weedon.

NOTTINGHAMSHIRE
Corner House Antiques
Queen St., Collingham, Nr. Newark.
East Bridgeford Antiques
Main St., East Bridgeford.
Markham Moor Antiques
Markham Moor, Nr. Retford.
Castle Antiques
25 Castle St., & Bairds Malt,
Northgate, Newark.
T.T. Antiques
11 Strawberry Hall Lane & Castle Hall,
Castle Gate, Newark.
Trent Antiques
48 Castlegate, Newark.
Curios
12 Alfreton Rd., Nottingham.
Tall House Antiques
The Old Country Furniture Shop,
6 Market Place, Tuxford.

OXFORDSHIRE
The Pine Corner Shop
Chapel Square, Deddington.

Market Place Antiques
35 Market Place, Henley-on-Thames.
Gems
222 Abingdon Road, Oxford.
M. Preston
35 South Parade, Oxford.
Maeve Clowes Antiques
Windmill Farm House,
High St., Watlington.
Country Style
The Triangle, London Rd., Wheatley.

SHROPSHIRE
Antiques Pine
Shop 14, High St., Ellesmere.

SOMERSET
The Pendulum,
Avenue Arcade, Bridgewater.
Grange Court Antiques
Corfe, Nr. Taunton.
Chez Chalon (Furniture) Ltd.
10 Church St., Crewkerne.
Susannes
45 Catherine St., Frome.
West Country Pine,
98 Church St., Highbridge.
Herald House Antiques
North St., Langport.
Milverton Antiques
Fore St., Milverton.

STAFFORDSHIRE
Anvil Antiques
41 St. Edwards St., Leek.

SUFFOLK
Edmunds Antiques
128 Southgate St., Bury St. Edmunds.
Michaels Moore Antiques
The Old Court, Nethergate St., Clare.
Brownhouse Antiques
Ipswich Rd., Claydon, Nr. Ipswich.
Richmond House
Fressingfield, Nr. Diss.
The Antique Shop
Hacheston, Nr. Wickham Market.
Blyth Bygones
8 Station Rd., Halesworth.
St. Jacobs Hall,
Laxfield, Nr. Woodbridge.
The Little Gallery
Long Melford.

SURREY
Furniture Finds
The Barn, High St., Bramley.
Antics
44 Portsmouth Rd., Cobham.
Woodgoods Ltd.
Hale Farm, Farnham.
Country Junk
34 Meadrow, Farncombe, Godalming.

SUSSEX
Shop of the Yellow Frog
14a Westbourne St., Brighton.

Michael Carmichael
Brook House, Horsebridge,
Nr. Hailsham.
Mary Salter
East St., Lewes.
Ann Lingard
Rope Walk Antiques, Rye.
Country Mood
The Old Coach House, 4 Tarrant Sq.,
Arundel.
Pine & Design Gallery
Haywards Heath Rd., Balcombe.
Bimbo
Knockhundred Row, Midhurst.
Digby Antiques
Buck House, South Harting,
Nr. Petersfield.
Sandhill Barn Antiques
Washington.
Pine Oast
Burwash.

TYNE & WEAR
Country Style
23-29 High Bridge St.,
Newcastle-upon-Tyne.

WARWICKSHIRE
Roger Jones
Antiques & Adams Antiques
The Old School, Alderminster.
The Old Rectory
Loxley, Nr. Stratford-upon-Avon.
Birmingham Antiques
8 Church St., Shipston-on-Stour.
Bury Antiques
2 The Bury, Off Sheep St.,
Shipston-on-Stour

WEST MIDLANDS
Pine Wood
192 Faleshill Rd., Coventry.

YORKSHIRE NORTH
The Attic
7 Station Parade, Harrogate.

Kindon Antiques
38 Forest Lane Head, Harrogate.
W.T. & J. Spencer
Arundel House, Lower Bentham.
Pine Finds
Shippen Bower, Marton-cum-Grafton,
Nr. York.
Primrose Antiques
Chapel Hill, Skipton.
Pond Cottage Antiques
Bransby Rd., Stillington.
Clewlow Antiques
102 Walmgate, York.

YORKSHIRE WEST
Aberford Antiques Ltd.
Hicklam House, Aberford.
Manor Barn Pine
Main St., Addingham, Nr. Ilkley.
H. K. White Ltd.
Cottingley Bridge, Bingley.
Georgiana Antiques
32-36 Bondgate, Otley.

SCOTLAND
Mostly Pine
The Smithy, Tomatin, Inverness-shire.
The Old Bakery
St. Cyrus, Nr. Montrose,
Kincardineshire.
Carolyn Scott Antiques & Curios
16 Victoria St., Edinburgh.

WALES
Kings Head Antiques
8 Rivulet Rd., Wrexham.
Gladstone House Antiques
Manod Old School,
Blaenau Ffestiniog.
Rodney Adams Antiques
Hall Place, 10 Penlan St., Pwllheli.
The Hay Galleries Ltd.
4 High Town, Hay-on-Wye.
W. S. & J. B. Cayless
Maesgwn Farm, Trecastle.

100